singing windows

Gabriel, Michaelhouse School Chapel, Balgowan, Natal, South Africa

Adapted from Nuit de Noel, Henri Matisse, Museum of Modern Art, New York

The Annunciation, East Harling, Norfolk, England

singing windows

written and illustrated
by mary young

abingdon press

new york   nashville

Library of Congress Catalog Card Number: 62-7869

Chapel of the Rosary by Matisse, Vence, France

CONTENTS

Chartres

On a high hill in the little town of Chartres, France, fifty-five miles southwest of Paris, there stands a beautiful cathedral. For almost 800 years it has been a source of strength to those nearby and an inspiration to the thousands who have come from all over the world to see its beauty. This cathedral is renowned for its windows. No other church in the world has as fine a collection of medieval stained glass. As the sun shines on the windows, they sing of the glory of God and the hopes and achievements of man.

Long before the traveler reaches the little town on the Eure River, he can see the spires of the cathedral reaching heavenward. The two towers were built in different centuries, and they are not alike. Strangely enough, the smaller is the more famous. It rises with strength and proportion from a square tower to an octagonal spire. It is thought by many to be the most beautiful spire in all the world.

Chartres consists of an upper and lower town connected by some very steep and twisting streets. On the way to the cathedral the traveler passes a flour mill, a dyeing and leather shop, a factory making farm machinery, another making hosiery, and even a place where artists still work in glass.

Beyond these shops is the cathedral itself. The first view is of the façade with its three lancet windows, rose window, and on either side a flanking tower that rises up into a spire. Inside, the first impression is of beauty of color. The walls glow with the rich colors of the glass windows, those of the façade, of the high windows on the walls of the nave, and of the apse. The coloring changes with the season and the hour. When evening comes and the last rays of the sun creep through, it is as if the walls are strewn with gold. The windows to the north contain more blue and those to the south are flushed with red and orange. There are 176 of them in all, and most of them date back to the twelfth and thirteenth centuries.

The cathedral at Chartres was built to honor Mary, the mother of Jesus. The story of the cathedral begins in about the fourth century. At that time the people of Chartres built a small Christian church on the site of an old Druid shrine. This church was destroyed by fire several centuries later and a second church was built in the ninth century. It, too, burned and so did the one built to replace it. Each time a

From a French picture Bible, 1250

new church was built, it was more beautiful than the one before. Finally in the eleventh century Chartres had a beautiful Gothic church that was the joy of all the people. Then in 1134 a terrible fire destroyed the whole west end of this church and it was fifteen years before it was rebuilt. Again in 1194 there was another great fire. This swept through the entire town. People left their burning homes to save their favorite window in the cathedral, *"La Dame de la Belle Verriere"* (the lady of the beautiful window). The fire destroyed all but the new west end and this one window.

The people of Chartres loved their church so much that they started at once to rebuild the cathedral. Men, women, and children carried stones, some harnessing themselves to the carts to carry material. Kings, nobles, merchants, craftsmen, and peasants all did what they could. Some gave money, others worked with their hands; but with all their efforts, it was 1260 before the new church was finally completed and the beautiful window which they had saved from the fire more than fifty years before was once again placed in the front of the church.

This oldest window is still considered to be the most beautiful window at Chartres. But many other lovely windows were made to enrich the fine new structure. Just beyond the Madonna and Child is a

9

"Tree of Jesse" window which rates next in beauty. It portrays the lineage of Jesus. The figure of Jesse lies at the foot of the window and from his loins rises the "tree," a mass of interweaving scroll work with foliage spreading over the entire window, carrying on its branches David and other human ancestors of Christ, and culminating in the Virgin and Christ, himself, at the top of the window. On either side are the prophets foretelling his coming, surrounded by a rich border of color.

Three great windows with many panels show the life of Christ from the annunciation to the resurrection. In addition there are the stories of the Good Samaritan, the Prodigal Son, Jonah, Abraham, Saul, Melchisedek, Habakkuk, Adam and Eve, John the Baptist, the men on the road to Emmaus, the history of Paul, the story of the apostles, and the Last Judgment.

The Furriers, Chartres, France

The Prodigal Son window has always been one of the most popular windows. It shows the younger son asking the father for his inheritance and then going by horseback to Paris where he is met by two young women. Evidently the artists thought of Paris as the "far country of wrong." The son is seen feasting and having a good time and then being dragged out of a house by devils. He is pictured knocking acorns from the trees in order to feed the swine. At last he decides to return to his father's house and there follows the homecoming scene.

In addition to the Bible stories, the life of Charlemagne is recorded in glass, and even the legends of some of his family. You can read the history of France, the stories of her kings and queens, her romances, her wars, her triumphs, and her defeats.

Even the donors and their crafts are represented in the windows. Over forty craftsmen are shown at their daily tasks. The butcher is pictured with his assistant slicing meat with a long knife, while a customer is pointing a finger at them. The baker is pictured with a basket of bread and with him is a customer who evidently has just bought five loaves. A tailor displays his goods to two young gentlemen while his assistant is seen measuring off some cloth. A furrier shows his fur pieces to two young ladies and a shoemaker is pictured cutting leather and making shoes. A fishmonger is seen with his two-wheeled cart. Thus the windows tell the story of men in various walks of life who long ago loved their Lord and their church, and gave gifts to build the great cathedral.

During the fifty years of building, many exciting things took place in the world. It was the time of the Crusades, when pilgrims were trying to gain control of Jerusalem. Louis IX was king of France; King John in England was forced to sign the Magna Charta; Roger Bacon was

11

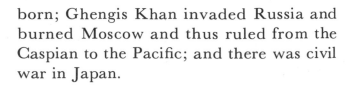

born; Ghengis Khan invaded Russia and burned Moscow and thus ruled from the Caspian to the Pacific; and there was civil war in Japan.

Since 1240 the great cathedral has stood fast. Through fires, lightning, cannon balls, and revolutions, its windows have told their ageless tales. At least twice the great church has been threatened with destruction. Once in 1591 Henry IV, King of Navarre and determined to be king of France, was fighting at Chartres. During the siege he heard the bells of the cathedral and, inquiring, learned that the people were celebrating an anniversary of a former siege. Henry was so moved that he ordered his guns silent for the entire day. He renewed the attack the next day and eventually took the town, but without damaging the great cathedral. Another time during the French Revolution the cathedral was ordered destroyed. The work of destruction was begun, but because no one would allow his property to be used as a base of operations, the cathedral again was saved. The enemy has battered at its gates, plague and famine have swept through the land, but the great cathedral on the hill still stands.

James Russell Lowell once wrote:
"I gaze around on the windows, pride of France!
Each the bright gift of some mechanic guild,
Who loved their city and thought gold well spent
To make her beautiful with piety."

Solomon,
Chartres, France

The history of

Stained Glass

The traditional story of the discovery of glass is by Pliny, the Roman historian. He tells that about 2000 B.C., some Phoenician sailors were shipwrecked on a beach in Assyria. When they went ashore to cook their meal, they were unable to find any rocks on which to place the cooking vessels. Everything was white sand. The sailors went back to the shipwrecked boat and returned with some lumps of natron, a kind of soda, which they used as a support for the pots over the fire. Later, after the fire was burned down, the men noticed a shining brittle substance. This substance was glass which had been made by the fire, the soda, and the sand. From then on glass was made by melting sand and soda together.

It does not seem likely that an open fire would be hot enough to produce glass, but this is the way the story was told. Whatever really happened, it would appear that the earliest producer of larger quantities of glass was Egypt. Egypt has a limitless supply of sand and rich deposits of natron. By using a core of sand and weaving long threads of hot glass around it, the Egyptians made many beautiful articles, some of which can be seen in museums today. Glass became so common that the average family had several glass pieces. And the glass products were so beautiful that soon Phoenician traders took them to Greece, and later Rome, to exchange for other merchandise.

15

Once glass was shipped to other countries, others discovered how to make it. Soon Egypt was no longer the center of glass-making. Instead, Rome became the center. But glass was also made in Greece. Those who traveled from Greece to Rome told of how mosaic pictures were made of glass in Greece. These mosaics were really the forerunner of the stained or colored glass windows.

Mosaics were made by fitting small pieces of colored glass into damp plaster to make a picture or design. At first the edges of the glass were left rough, and when the light struck them the effect was dazzling. Later, when workers tried to improve on their mosaics by smoothing off the rough edges, some of the beauty was lost and the art declined.

Although mosaics were made many years before the birth of Christ, it was the Christian church that brought about the widespread use of mosaics. Mosaics of Christ and the apostles, and Bible stories were a part of the early Christian churches. In the fourth century the Emperor Constantine built a great church in Constantinople whose interior was almost entirely covered by glass mosaics. Travelers and missionaries seeing this beautiful church went back to their

16

AAGNES: ☩SCA

*St. Agnes, San Apollinare
Nuovo, Ravenna, Italy*

The Ascension, Le Mans Cathedral, Le Mans, France

Notre-Dame de la Belle Verriere, Chartres Cathedral, Chartres, France

Chapter House, Westminster Abbey, London, England

homes and at the first opportunity built mosaics into their churches.

As the church grew and spread, its organization became more complex. By the fifth century most of the Christian countries were divided into districts or dioceses, each presided over by a bishop. Each bishop had his headquarters at a large church in his area, called a *cathedral*.

The Latin word, *cathedra*, means seat or chair. Thus a cathedral was the place where the bishop of the district sat, and his chair was in the apse of the church. This church was the most important one in the district and was the center of not only religious life but also civic activities.

By the ninth and tenth centuries bishops were beginning to take great pride in building beautiful churches in their districts. There was a great deal of rivalry to outdo one another in the size and beauty of cathedrals. By this time, too, people had begun to build churches in a different style. No longer did they have domed wooden roofs that were ideal for mosaic pictures. Instead the churches had sloping high ceilings with windows along the side. This was called Gothic architecture, and in the Gothic church there was little space on which mosaics could be placed.

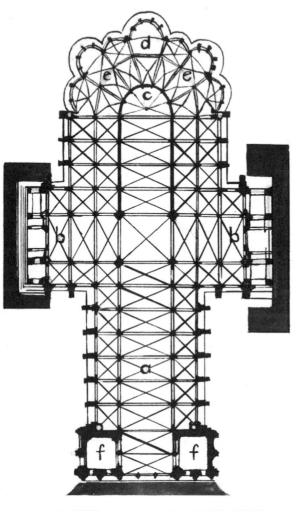

A. NAVE
B. TRANSEPT
C. APSE
D. AMBULATORY
E. CHEVET
F. TOWER

The Gothic cathedral is in the shape of a cross. The space that represents the arms of the cross is called the *transept*. The long, usually narrow section in the center under the highest part of the roof is called the *nave*. The section that extends beyond the transept is called the *apse*. In some periods the apse was semicircular and at other times it was square or octagonal. The aisles surrounding the apse are *ambulatories* and the *chevet* is the apse, ambulatories, and small chapels off the ambulatories. The walls of a cathedral are divided into three stories: the *ground floor*, the *triforium* with four arched openings, and the *clerestory*. Windows cover the walls of the clerestory, aisles, transepts, and apse.

Because there was little blank wall space in these Gothic buildings, workmen adapted the mosaic idea to the windows. They substituted lead for plaster, and made a decoration even richer than before. Elaborate design of colored glass, held together in lead, soon appeared in many church windows. Borders were made of rich colors, used very much like gems. Colors took on special meanings, and certain designs meant strength or conquest or place of birth or some family tradition. As far back as the time of Moses, banners had been used to designate different tribes or camps. The same idea was now put into stained glass, and almost every church had windows designed in patterns that had special meanings.

Soon the artists learned that they could make designs in glass that would not only inspire but instruct, and they began to make windows that told the story of the church and the stories of the Bible. These windows served as textbooks for those who had no books and for those who could not read. Anyone who could see could look at the windows and understand the ancient stories. Those who saw the life of Christ told in windows could tell the story to others, and these could bring it to still others who had not heard it.

Two of the earliest windows with story pictures can still be seen in the Augsburg Cathedral in Germany and in the Cathedral at Le Mans in France. King David and the prophets are pictured in the Augsburg window, and the Ascension of Christ is pictured in the window at Le Mans. Both of these

King David, Augsburg, Germany

are thought to date from the eleventh century. The figure of Christ is absent from the Ascension window, that part having been lost. The central figure is Mary, the mother of Jesus, who, some believe, was present at the ascension. The twelve apostles are with her, looking upward. These windows were forerunners of the Golden Age of Stained Glass.

19

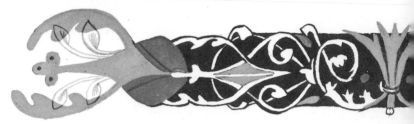

The twelfth and thirteenth centuries are thought of as the Golden Age of Stained Glass in France, for it was in this period that the art developed. Many new churches were built. The colored glass was attracting more and more attention, and each bishop was trying to find new and better ways of making his church the most beautiful and instructive in all the land.

The windows of this period are known for their rich ornamental borders, looking very much like oriental rugs. The colors were yellow, blue, white, red, and green, but were spoken of as sapphire, pearl, ruby, and emerald. Blue was the all-important color for it gave light to the window and was used where needed regardless of what was pictured. A dog or even a person's hand might be blue. The glass pieces were small, most of them not more than a half inch wide and one or two inches long. Even the very largest were no bigger than the palm of a hand.

During the Golden Age, a series of pictures was used to tell a story. They were held together within an iron framework. The artist added to the design by painting on the glass the features, such as hair, hands, and the folds of the garments. This not only added beauty but aided in understanding the story pictured.

Workmen of this time usually made their windows in the churchyard as the church was being built. Along one side of the churchyard were the fires of the blowers of glass. Into the kettles of dull sand, lime, and soda, certain chemicals were dropped that transformed the liquid into blues, reds, greens, and golds. Then the glass blower would gather up on his pipe a blob of the liquid and blow a cylinder of glass which was later flattened into a thin sheet. The best glass was seldom more than one eighth of an inch thick.

On the other side of the courtyard the artist worked at his table, which was usually twice the length of the window. Because paper was too expensive to use, the artist scraped chalk on the table and sprinkled the powdered chalk with water to form a paste in which the design was drawn. The lead supports, or cames, were an integral part of the design and were drawn in first. Then sections of the picture were marked for various colors and then the glass was cut to fit the pattern. To cut a piece of glass to the desired size, a piece of oiled string was placed on the glass where the break was desired. The string was then set on fire. The glass was heated along the desired break by the burning string and then was plunged into cold water where it would break as planned. Finally the edges of the broken glass were smoothed and fitted into the cames. Then the whole was weatherproofed with cement. When all the pieces were cut and leaded together, the window was finished.

Not all stained glass windows were alike. There were many kinds. The Rose Window was one of the earliest kinds to be made and was popular for many centuries. You may have one in your church or in your community. It is a round window with a center and lines extending in the shape of the petals of a flower. Perhaps the rose windows at the Notre Dame Cathedral in Paris are the most famous. They were made in the thirteenth century.

From the early rose windows there developed a similar window called a "Wheel Window." In the center is a picture of a shield and the radiating panels contain different designs in glass.

"The Jesse Window" was another early form of design. It consists of a twisting vine that covers the whole window and portrays the genealogy of Christ, from the line of David. There may be as few as four or five figures and as many as fifty. The vine always starts with Jesse and ends at the top with Christ. At Sens Cathedral the Jesse window is a little different for it not only honors the ancestors of Jesus, but a donkey can be seen on one of the branches. It is thought to honor the animal that played so great a part in the life of Christ.

"Belt Windows" are groups of long panel windows each having a central figure or figures in bright colors. The figures form a line across all the windows, resembling a belt. The background glass is usually white or light colored. The figures are most often single, each one a prophet, apostle, or early Christian.

At the time the first richly colored windows of the thirteenth century were in style, another type of window called the "Grisaille" window was also being made. This type of window was made up largely of glass that was white or light in color, with a colored border and some color here and there throughout the window. Delicate patterns were painted on the glass. These windows were developed perhaps to give more light in the sanctuary, and of course could be produced more cheaply. The "Five Sisters" windows at York Minster are the outstanding examples of the Grisaille type.

Belt window, Exeter Cathedral, Exeter, England; Grisaille window, Lincoln Cathedral, England; Jesse window, Chartres, France; Rose window, Chartres, France.

"rose"

"grisaille"

"belt"

"Jesse"

King Charles I, Magdalen College Hall, Oxford, England

The "Perpendicular" style first became popular in the fifteenth century. The most beautiful windows in England today are in this style. Regular patterns running vertically took the place of flowing geometrical patterns. Helmets, shields, and mottoes were pictured in rich detail and color. Westminster Abbey is known for its beautiful perpendicular style windows.

Stained glass windows did not come to England as soon as they did to the Continent. During the Golden Age in France, Chartres was the chief center for stained glass art, and the people went there to learn from the masters. From Chartres, artists eventually went to England, but the windows they produced there were of a different type. Most of the windows were of white glass with figures painted on them. Perhaps this was because there was need for more light on dark dreary days, or perhaps there was a difference in national taste, or a greater need for economy.

The cathedrals of Canterbury and York contain the most ancient stained glass in England. The oldest dates from the latter part of the thirteenth century. Little of this old glass is left, however, because the Puritans, who ruled in the sixteenth century, opposed the use of stained glass. Only a remnant escaped destruction at their hands. The name of Richard Culmer heads the list of those who were most active in this destruction. He was in charge of Canterbury Cathedral at one time, and it is told that he stood on a ladder sixty steps high and with a pike in hand "rattled down proud Becket's glassie bones." It was Thomas A. Becket who had suggested that the windows be made, several centuries earlier. Culmer, at least, thought the windows important enough to destroy. There were those who later sold the glass just for the price of the lead in them. Because of these men there are very few complete windows of early English glass.

24

It was near the end of the fourteenth or early in the fifteenth century that the word "stained" was first used. After a picture was painted on the glass, a stain was used so that when it was fired in a kiln various shades of yellow resulted. "Stained Glass" has since been used to include all colored glass windows.

As long as the Gothic style of church architecture was popular, stained glass art thrived. However, in the fourteenth century a great disease known as the Black Death or Black Plague swept across the land and disorganized the life of the people. Hundreds of thousands died of the disease. Whole towns were wiped out. The arts and sciences were neglected, the art of stained glass was almost forgotten, and formulas were lost forever.

Churches built in the sixteenth century were simple columned structures, and fewer windows were needed. During this period large pieces of glass with painted designs were used instead of the small bits of glass which had typified the stained glass windows for centuries.

The sixteenth century was the period of the Renaissance, and there were many changes taking place in every sphere of life. These changes were soon reflected in the pictures produced in stained glass. People had become richer, and they were less interested in the Bible and more interested in themselves. A nobleman often had his picture put in glass with small circles of flowers, birds, or butterflies painted around him. Sir Walter Raleigh's portrait was done in stained glass and placed in a popular inn. Around his picture were painted various emblems of his wanderings, such as a tobacco plant, sea lions, and parrots.

In the Cathedral of Troyes, built at this time, the story of the creation was portrayed in stained glass. The world is shown as a rotating ball being fashioned by God. It is a little more complete in each of a series of panels until at last it is shown in finished form. Then come Adam and Eve, other stories of the Old Testament, and on through the New Testament. At the very top of the window the cross appears between the two thieves.

The sixteenth century marked the end of the great interest in stained glass. By the close of the seventeenth century its manufacture was almost forgotten. There was little interest again until the middle of the nineteenth century.

When the first colonists crossed the Atlantic to America, there was no need for stained glass windows. Their life was simple. Homes and churches were made of logs cut down by the men themselves. The Pilgrims could read, and they brought Bibles with them from England, so there was no need for the storytelling glass.

In the nineteenth century, however, Americans began building Gothic-type churches. And with Gothic churches came stained glass windows. Craftsmen visited the early Cathedrals in Europe and were astonished at the beauty of the stained glass. They returned with a desire to recapture the glory of those windows. After much research they were able to produce windows technically as fine as those seen in France.

Even though the Gothic type of church architecture is not used as much today as it was, the interest in colored glass has not lessened. In fact, it is being employed more and more.

Today's windows do not take so long to make as the windows of old. If a church today wants a stained glass window, an idea is submitted to the Church Board. Small

Adapted from
Wooden relief panels donated by Stained
Glass Industries, Washington, D.C.

colored sketches are made scaled to the size of the opening. When these are approved, the artist makes up full-sized black and white drawings which are called *cartoons*. From the cartoon, two paper patterns are made. One is an outline drawing showing the leadlines and the shape of the glass to be cut. The other is a similar drawing cut into pieces the actual shape of the glass. These serve as guides for cutting the stained glass. The pattern left whole will be used in assembling the pieces to see that the design fits perfectly.

Great care is used in selecting the glass. Some of the glass is imported, but more and more of it is made in factories in the United States. When the glass is chosen, the paper patterns are placed on it, and it is cut to the shape desired with a diamond or steel wheel.

After the glass has been cut, the painter starts to work. He paints

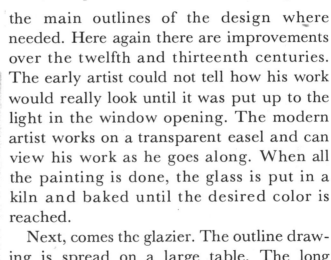

the main outlines of the design where needed. Here again there are improvements over the twelfth and thirteenth centuries. The early artist could not tell how his work would really look until it was put up to the light in the window opening. The modern artist works on a transparent easel and can view his work as he goes along. When all the painting is done, the glass is put in a kiln and baked until the desired color is reached.

Next, comes the glazier. The outline drawing is spread on a large table. The long strips of wide lead are placed on the black heavy lines and the glass fitted into the lead. The joints are soldered and the window cemented on both sides to make it firm and waterproof. Sometimes the window is made as a whole and sometimes in sections that are assembled when the window is installed in the church.

Nehemiah, Washington Cathedral, Washington, D.C.

All of the styles that appeared in early churches, and many new ones, are represented in the stained glass windows being made in America today.

In our national capital, the Washington Cathedral has windows equal to those done in medieval times. The artists have copied the formulas, methods, and thought to make the windows as rich, informative, and inspiring as those at Chartres. As in France and England, the history and life of our nation are pictured in these windows. And like the twelfth and thirteenth century windows, the stories and characters of the Bible are portrayed. The Garden of Eden window shows an angel with a flaming sword driving Adam and Eve out of the garden. God's search for man and man's search for God is portrayed in a window in which Jacob is wrestling with an angel. Underneath is Jacob's dream at Bethel. Other Biblical windows show Moses on Mt. Sinai with the Ten Commandments; the life story of Daniel; God speaking to Saul on the Damascus road; and finally God speaking to the missionary who translated the Bible into the Chinese language.

There are three large windows in the Washington Cathedral representing the Good Neighbor policy among nations. The English window is known as the "Prayer Book Window" for it shows the history of the English prayer book and the power of prayer. The Canadian window represents things as important to that country. The third window represents South America. Simon Bolivar, the George Washington of South America, is in the center and on one side a statesman from Argentina and on the other side one from Brazil. At the top is "Christ of the Andes" and in small figures are plants, animals, and natives of various countries of South America.

The American Labor Organizations have made possible three beautiful windows in this cathedral. As the guilds of old put their trademarks in some way in the windows they donated, so have the labor unions put their seals and symbols in the borders of these windows.

Ruth is the main figure in the "Agricultural and Maritime" window. She is holding a sheaf of grain. In the left lancet is Peter the fisherman, the fishing boats of New England, and the gathering of the grapes in Naboth's vineyard. In the right lancet is Joseph as a shepherd boy tending his father's flocks and a modern farm scene.

In the "Industrial and Social Reform" window Nehemiah is the central figure. The Israelites are shown rebuilding the walls and temple at Jerusalem. Those instrumental in social reform are shown, and at the very top is the Christ child with arms outstretched offering to all men the love of God.

The third window of the Labor series is the "Artisan and Craftsmen" window. Christ, the carpenter, is in the center. In one hand he holds a saw and the other hand is raised in blessing. At his feet are symbols of present day building and industry.

The great Rose Window in the north wall contains more than 9,000 pieces of glass with red as the predominant color. The theme of the window is the Last Judgment, and Christ as the Judge is pictured in the center. In the sixteen petals and the eight medallions forming the rim, the pictures symbolize the Day of Judgment.

Another great American cathedral is St. John the Divine in New York City. The great Rose Window in the west front is one of the great windows of the world. It is forty feet in diameter and contains over 10,000 pieces of glass. Christ is the central figure of this window, and radiating from the center are different symbols of the Christian faith. The four petal units show the figures of the four evangelists.

The Crusaders window in one of the special bays of the cathedral, shows knights on horseback, armies, kings, children, and the Holy City, Jerusalem, for which the Crusaders fought. Pictures of modern crusaders, such as Milton, Wilberforce, and Reed, are shown in the bottom panels.

The Army is represented in the Vision of Constantine before the battle fought in 312; the Battle of Tours in 732; Washington at Valley Forge; and the Surrender of Burgoyne

Ronchamp Chapel, by Le Corbusier, Vosges, France

Royan Cathedral, Royan, France

in 1777. The Navy is represented also in major battles, which include the defeat of the Spanish Armada in 1588 and the Battle of Trafalgar in 1805. The small medallions show figures of Martel, Washington, Grant, Lee, Drake, Dewey and others. St. George and the Dragon is in the center medallion.

But these great cathedrals are not the only places where stained glass is being used today in America. All across the land churches are being built. They are quite often modern in design, and are small centers of natural beauty and simplicity. The architects have departed from the traditional patterns of construction and are building churches whose steep roofs almost touch the ground or whose peaked roofs are in a star shape. For these modern churches, artists are also experimenting with new techniques in colored glass. The old storytelling windows are being replaced by contemporary or religious symbolism in bright colors and abstract designs. The pieces of glass vary from small bits to large, rough hewn pieces that are set in cement, plaster, wood, or stainless steel.

Colored windows today are used in large settings or as small openings around the walls. Techniques have been developed so that the windows can be enjoyed at night as well as in the daylight and inscriptions read from the outside as well as from the inside. But as always, the stained glass windows are designed to harmonize with the architecture.

Hundreds of years and hundreds of artists have come and gone since the lovely windows were made in the courtyard at Chartres. Heavy boards with sketches in whitewash have been exchanged for glass easels and modern tools. Patterns are made of paper. Glass is made by modern methods, although these methods are sometimes based on old formulas. But the purposes, to tell a story or to create beauty, remain the same. Thus in this new era of stained glass, windows still sing of the glory of God and the works of man.

Nativity Scene, Chartres, France

St. Peter,
Gloucester Cathedral,
Gloucester, England

Mother and Child, Winchcombe, England

Mystical Wine Press, St. Etienne-du-Mont, Paris, France

Legends

Tales and legends pass from age to age, and from person to person. During the twelfth and thirteenth centuries commerce was pouring over all the roads and rivers; population was increasing; towns were growing; and all Europe was entering upon a great church building program. Wherever and whenever people gathered together, stories were told. And these stories were put in the stained glass of the churches. Some of the stories were Bible stories, others were stories of saints and martyrs, and still others were stories of battles and kings.

Some of the stories being told in the glass of great churches, whether they were built hundreds of years ago or just yesterday, can be told again and again and still retain the freshness and interest they held for those who first heard them. Some such stories are told in many windows in many churches in many countries.

CHARTRES

Much has already been said of the beautiful windows of Chartres, but so many of the stories told there are told again and again in the windows of great French cathedrals—Le Mans, Sens, Bourges, Tours, and many others—that Chartres seems a good place to begin.

33

Three Young Maidens

Three separate legends were told in the windows of Chartres about St. Nicholas, but there is one that is most familiar to children in America. It is the story of the Three Young Maidens.

Nicholas, who lived in Asia Minor, was left a fortune when his parents died; and after he became a priest and a bishop, he wondered how he could best use it. He looked around for those who needed his help. Among his neighbors was one who had three beautiful daughters. They had many suitors, but no offer of marriage; for they were too poor to have a dowry. They could not hope for marriage without a dowry. The father was so poor that the time came when he had to decide whether he would let them starve or sell them as slaves.

One night as the poor father was standing by an open window, thinking that on the morrow he would take his eldest daughter to be sold as a slave, a heavy object sailed past him and fell at his feet. He picked it up and could hardly believe his eyes. It was a moneybag. He opened it and gold pieces came rolling out. There were enough for a dowry for his oldest daughter. The next morning he told the good news to his daughter who ran to the market to buy clothes, jewelry, and food. That evening the youth who loved her came, and they were betrothed.

The father's joy did not last long for he soon thought of his second daughter who was as lovely as her older sister. The day came when he knew he would have to take her to the slave market. He stood at the window once more, thinking that a miracle could not happen again. But it did. In flew the moneybag and landed at his feet. He ran out of the house but was too late to see the person who had thrown it. The next day the second daughter became engaged to be married.

That night the father stood at the window again. Surely, he thought, the person who had provided for the other sisters would not neglect the youngest who was the most beautiful of all.

About the time that the gifts had arrived before, the father went out and hid himself in the bushes near the window. And before long a man approached with a moneybag in his hand. As he tossed it through the open window, the father ran out, seized the man's cloak, and began to thank him for his kindness. The giver was Nicholas and he made the father promise not to tell anyone about the gifts. The next day the youngest girl was engaged to be married.

No doubt the father tried to keep his promise, but secrets have a way of being told. Soon people everywhere were giving secret gifts in the name of St. Nicholas. Sometimes parents wishing to surprise their children put gifts in their shoes while they were asleep. The next morning the children would shout, "See what St. Nicholas brought me!" Soon the children were leaving shoes outside their doors so that St. Nicholas could leave the gifts without being seen. The custom and the story of good St. Nicholas spread to all Europe and then to America. But long before America was settled, or even discovered, in an age when there were no beautifully illustrated storybooks, children would gather on an afternoon in a cathedral and read the story of St. Nicholas in the colored windows.

Martin and the Beggar

At Chartres, Tours, Bourges, and at Canterbury in England, there are windows telling the story of Martin and the beggar. Martin, to please his father, became a soldier and worked hard to receive many promotions.

One day as Martin was riding through the city gates with his soldiers, a beggar stood nearby pleading for food and clothes. The other soldiers passed by without a glance, but Martin felt sorry for the man. Martin had no extra food or clothing to give the beggar, but he took his sword, cut his own cloak in two, and gave half of it to the shivering man.

That night as Martin slept, he had a dream. He saw Christ wearing the half cloak he had given to the beggar and heard him say, "Inasmuch as ye did it unto one of the least of these, ye did it unto me."

In the morning when he awoke, he remembered the dream. He sought out the leader of a group of Christians and was baptized. Two years later Martin secured his release from the army and began to preach and teach. He went to Poitiers and studied under the bishop there. He worked hard and gained favor with the people. When the position of Bishop of Tours was open, the people joined together and went to Martin to persuade him to be the new bishop. For the second time Martin did the

Adapted from
St. Martin and the Beggar by El Greco

thing he did not want to do. He became a bishop.

The Devil, people said, was always alert to test this great leader. One day as Martin was on his way to Rome, on foot, he met the Devil in person. The Devil ridiculed the preacher for serving a master who could not provide transportation for his workers. Martin turned on the Devil, made him into a mule, jumped on his back, and trotted off. The road was rough and the way long, and the Devil was soon sorry he had taunted Martin.

The people prayed that Martin might live forever. When he finally died they put his body in a boat and floated it toward Tours. Those who loved him said that the trees along the way burst into flowers and music was heard.

Roland and Ferragus

In the group of windows portraying the life of Charlemagne at the cathedral at Chartres is pictured the story of Roland. He was sometimes called Orlando and was the favorite nephew of Charlemagne. In one of the windows can be seen the giant Ferragus and Roland.

The legend is told that the giant's skin was so tough that no sword could make any impression on it. It was the custom of the giant to seize his oppressor and to carry him off. Roland decided to try to save the people from this wicked giant. Roland was strong and courageous in the battle. He was not captured, but his sword seemed useless on the giant. They fought until Ferragus became weary and suggested that they rest. A truce was made, and the giant lay down and immediately fell asleep. Roland felt so sorry for the exhausted Ferragus that he brought a stone and put it under his head. When the giant awoke, he was very grateful for the kindness shown him and became very friendly. He became so friendly with Roland that in their conversation he revealed that he could not be hurt except in one spot which was in the middle of his breast. Roland remembered this; and when the fight was renewed, he pierced the giant in the very spot that had been pointed out to him. So Ferragus was slain. There was much rejoicing when the people learned of the death of the wicked giant, and Roland was given much praise.

BOURGES

Next to Chartres, Bourges Cathedral has the most magnificent collection of stained glass in the world. The pieces of glass in the windows are so tiny that it must have taken years to make a single window. Many of the same stories are told at Bourges as at Chartres.

Legend of Bernard

A stained glass window at Bourges tells the story of Bernard who lived in the tenth century. Bernard was an only son of noble parents. He was well educated, and his parents hoped that someday he would become a knight and go off to do great deeds. Then one day his parents

learned that their son planned to become a priest. This was a great disappointment to them, and they decided that they would not allow him to do it. Instead, they had Bernard taken to a castle where a beautiful girl was waiting to become his bride.

Bernard, however, was determined to become a priest. The night before the wedding, he left a note, escaped onto a balcony, climbed the castle wall, and headed for the mountains. He spent the following years teaching and preaching.

Onc evening an old man and his wife came to Bernard's dwelling. They had heard of his great wisdom and had traveled many miles to seek his counsel. The aged couple told Bernard that they had had an only son whom they had adored and for whom they had had high hopes. The son had been about to be married when he had disappeared. They had never seen him or heard from him again. Bernard listened intently and, of course, recognized the couple as his parents, although they did not recognize him. He embraced them, telling them he was their long lost son. The happy parents stayed for many days; and when they returned to their home, they were content and pleased that their son had become such a good and useful man.

A Legend of India

Another story in the glass at Bourges, Chartres, and Tours is the story of Thomas. The legend, as it is told, concerns first of all a man named Gondoforus, King of India, who longed for a palace more beautiful than any in the world. He heard of Thomas, a great artist and builder, and invited him to come to build the palace. Thomas, when he

received the invitation, felt that this was an opportunity for him to take the message of Christ to India, and so he accepted.

After a long journey, Thomas arrived at the king's palace. The king explained the plans for the new palace and gave Thomas money for all the materials. While the work was to be done, Gondoforus went off on a tour of his kingdom.

Thomas was more interested in preaching than in building a palace; and when he found the people eager to hear what he had to say, he soon forgot all about why he had come. He spent all of his time preaching; and in the name of the king, he gave to the poor the money designated for the palace. It was not long until almost the entire city was converted to Christianity. Thomas was happy until the king returned to find his money gone and his palace unbuilt. He had Thomas thrown into prison and ordered him burned at the stake.

The night before the execution the brother of the king, who had been dead for a long time, appeared to him and told of the house with many mansions, the palace of gold and silver and jewels, that had been built for him in paradise. Thomas had given the king's money to help others and had preached the message of a heavenly life. He

had built for the king a heavenly palace that was far better than any earthly one. The king was so moved that he sent for Thomas and was baptized.

Three in a Tub

This legend is told not only once but several times in the windows of one cathedral. The interpretation and picture may vary, but all is credited to St. Nicholas. Both Bourges and Chartres have the story.

Once when Nicholas was Bishop of Myra, three boys wandered away one night in the woods. They finally came to an inn and asked for shelter. The innkeeper was a wicked man who stole from those who stayed with him. That night he searched the boys' clothes while they slept; but the boys had nothing to steal, so the innkeeper decided to take their clothes. Without their clothes, the boys looked all pink and tender like little pigs. Why, the man thought, wouldn't they be delicious pickled, even as the little pigs!

By morning the three little boys were lying in pickle bath in the salting-tub. Nearby, Bishop Nicholas had a dream in which he had seen all that had taken place at the inn. The next day he made a visit to the inn. When Nicholas was asked if he would care for something to eat, he replied that he would like some pork from the pickle-tub. The innkeeper was taken off guard. He turned white with fear and finally fell to the floor asking for mercy. St. Nicholas then went to the pickle barrel, prayed, and the scum on the brine parted and the heads of three little boys popped up. They never knew what had happened to them. The innkeeper wondered what would happen to him for his evil deed, but Nicholas, believing that nothing is ever past forgiveness, knelt down and prayed in thanksgiving. The innkeeper was pardoned, and he never pickled anyone again.

Many decisive battles were fought near Poitiers, and there is a wealth of history in the windows of the churches. The story is told of how Clovis, the Frank, met Alaric, the Visigoth, in battle in the sixth century. Clovis was a Christian who did not think it was right that the Visigoths, who were unbelievers, should control as much of Gaul as they did. Clovis won the battle, and the country became Christian.

Other windows tell of the battle in the eighth century when the Arabs and the Christians fought near Poitiers. The Arabs wanted to convert Europe to the Muslim religion. Charles Martel, known as Charles the Hammer, was the leader of the Christians who were finally victorious. Never after that did the Arabs try to bring Islam into France. This battle was fought about five miles from the city. In France it is called the Battle of Poitiers, but in our history books it is known as the Battle of Tours.

A Patient German Princess

Among the legends portrayed in the windows at Poitiers is the story of Radegund. She was a German princess, a daughter of a Thuringian king. When Radegund was born, Thuringia was ruled by three brothers. One day one of the three murdered Radegund's father, defeated the others, and became ruler of all three kingdoms. The new king, an uncle of Radegund, treated his

niece kindly, thinking she might someday be a bride for his son.

When Radegund was ten years old, Thuringia went to war with the French. During the war Radegund was taken captive by Clotaire, a Frankish king, and later became one of his wives. He was a cruel man; it is told that he murdered some of his own children. Fortunately, Radegund was left much to herself. She found her only joy in helping the sick, taking care of the poor, and teaching cleanliness. She spent much time in prayer. She was soon loved by the people and was so good and patient that even her evil husband stood in awe of her.

After many years of faithfulness, Radegund learned that her husband had murdered her only brother. She fled to Tours to ask Bishop Martin for help. He heard her story and soon found a place for her where she could work among the poor.

Eventually Radegund moved to Poitiers where she also spent her time teaching and helping others. She was instrumental in having public baths available for the common people. Once Clotaire, after many years of silence, decided to force his wife to return to him. Radegund, frightened by the threats of her husband, wrote to the Bishop of Paris, who interceded in her behalf and Clotaire never bothered her again. When Radegund died, the people said her face was still as lovely as a flower.

CATHEDRALS IN AND NEAR PARIS

The Cathedral of Notre Dame, built in the twelfth and thirteenth centuries, contains three famous Rose Windows, one of which is probably the finest erected in the thirteenth century. This is the Northern Rose Window which occupies approximately 1,300 square feet. It contains pictures of eighty characters from the Old Testament. In the center of the window, the Virgin Mary holds the child Jesus on her knees. The sixteen prophets who foretold the coming of the Saviour surround her, each holding a scroll which bears his name. The framework of the window is so intricate that it is hardly visible from the floor below.

44

The Western Rose Window, which is six feet smaller in radius than the northern window, is also of the thirteenth century. It has suffered from the weather and a lack of care for more than 700 years. Its beauty was also marred when, in the eighteenth century, the organ was attached to its frame concealing a part of the rose.

Tourists are more often attracted to the Southern Rose Window. The figure of Christ is in the center, surrounded by his apostles. The most precious glass of the cathedral, pure twelfth century blue, salvaged from an earlier window, is in the outer circle. In this beautiful blue glass the story of St. Matthew is told.

The Sainte Chapelle near the Cathedral of Notre Dame has often been referred to as the "Jewel Box," for it was made almost entirely of stained glass. Louis IX built it in the thirteenth century. Some windows have as many as 120 scenes, and altogether the windows of the chapel are said to have 1,134 scenes, most of which are stories from the Bible.

Not far from Paris is the Cathedral of St. Denis named for the first Bishop of Paris. This is the cathedral where the kings of France finally came to rest. It is thought to have the most ancient glass of any cathedral in France. The first Abbot of this cathedral was fascinated by the brilliance of stained glass and brought the best artists he could find to make the windows.

St. Denis

One window pictures Denis, one of the earliest Christian martyrs, who is said to have lived in the third century. He and two of his companions, who were deacons, were arrested by the government because they were Christians. Witnesses were hired to testify against them, and St. Denis and his friends were sentenced to death. The three escaped and for several years preached in the marshes around Paris. At last they were hunted down and brought to trial. Denis, bleeding from the stones and whiplashes of a violent crowd, was brought to the hill now called Montmartre, which means Mount of the Martyr. The soldiers made him kneel and, with one swift stroke of a sword, severed Denis's head from his body.

The head rolled in the dirt, and some legends say that boys kicked the head back and forth over the ground. In order to save his head, Denis picked it up and carried it four miles. He finally laid it down at a crossroads where he also laid his body, and there he has rested these hundreds of years.

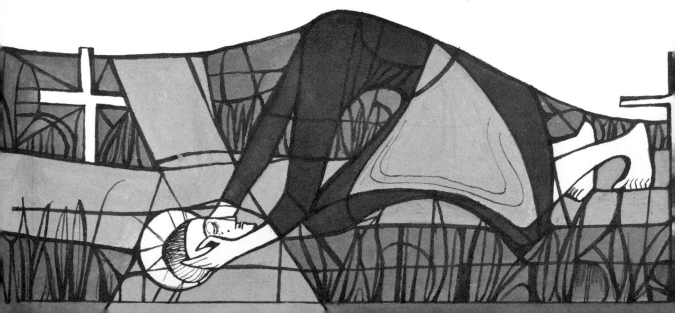

CANTERBURY

The Cathedral at Canterbury, England, and the one at Sens in France have much in common for the life of St. Thomas a Becket is pictured in each. The English priest spent four years at Sens, in exile from England. While there, he persuaded William of Sens to go to Canterbury and rebuild the cathedral which had been destroyed by fire. This was the beginning of Gothic architecture in England.

The windows portraying the life and works of St. Thomas at Canterbury also reveal the life of the times. In one window are some little boys throwing stones at frogs, three of which are quite large and green. One little boy has fallen into the water. There are other windows telling the stories of Patrick who was cured of his toothache; a man who gave away his clothes as a thank offering for being cured of leprosy; a priest who was cured of paralysis; and many others who came to St. Thomas to be healed.

Chaucer's Canterbury Tales are supposed to have been told by travelers on their way to visit Becket's tomb. The poet tells of stopping at cathedrals and even at inns where stories could be read in stained glass windows:

"And sooth to sayn, my chamber was
Full well depainted, and with glass
Were all the windows well y-glazed
Full clear, and not an hole y-crazed,
That to behold it was great joy:
For wholly all the story of Troy
Was in the glazing y-wrought thus,
Of Hector, and of King Laomedon,
And eke of Medea, and Jason;
Of Paris, Helen, and of Lavine."

*Arms of Henry VII, Cassio-
bury, England*

St. Yves Le Justicier by Gabriel Loire, France

Harlequine by Edward Veers, England

John the Evangelist, Winchester Chapel, Winchester, England

Grisaille window, Glasgow Cathedral, Glasgow, Scotland

The most beautiful windows at Canterbury are those depicting Bible stories. Some of these are fine examples of "type and antitype" windows, found also in other cathedrals. Down the center of each window is a picture from the life of Christ; on each side are "types" or subjects from the Old Testament that refer to his life. One window shows the Magi following the star; on one side is Balaam with the words, "There shall come a star out of Jacob"; and on the other side Isaiah with the words, "The Gentiles shall come to Thy light and kings to the brightness of Thy rising." The Magi appear before Herod, and on one side are the Israelites coming out of Egypt, led by Moses, and on the other side the Gentiles leaving a heathen temple containing an idol and following Christ.

Next the Magi make their offering to the infant Christ, and on one side is the Queen of Sheba visiting Solomon and on the other Joseph in Egypt receiving his brethren. There are twelve type and antitype windows in all, and they form one of the most elaborate sets of this type of window to be found. They include not only the life of Christ, but many of his parables which are not often found in stained glass. Two panels show the story of the Parable of the Sower, with the seed falling among the thorns and by the wayside.

There are windows of Enoch, Solomon and the Queen of Sheba, Eli and Samuel, Jonah, Lot, Jeroboam, Moses, and many others. There is also a beautiful window showing the cardinal virtues: Prudence is shown with a serpent in the right hand and two doves in the left; Justice is shown stooping forward with a pair of scales in one hand and a scroll in the other; Temperance is shown with a flaming torch in the right hand and in the left, a bowl of water; Fortitude, the fourth virtue, has a sword in one hand and a twisted cord in the other, which some think is a serpent.

YORK MINSTER

York Minster in England is also famous for its windows. At least five churches have been built on the site of the one now standing. Like Canterbury and other great churches, it was often destroyed by fire because there were many wooden buildings nearby and fire fighting was almost unknown.

The most famous window at York is the "Five Sisters" window. Some feel it is unsurpassed in the world. It is a "grisaille" window and has been referred to as a "dream of silvery light" and a "shimmering mass of pearl and silver." Legend says that five sisters wove a tapestry design, and that same design was made into stained glass. At the center is a round medallion showing Daniel in the lions' den. Daniel is being fed by the prophet Habakkuk, who is being lowered into the den by an angel. Only one lion is shown, and he is lying on the floor. Other sections of the group show the figures of St. Stephen and St. Laurence holding the symbols of their martyrdom, and in the center is St. Christopher with the child Jesus on his shoulder.

Christopher and the Child

Christopher wanted to serve only the mightiest man on earth and started out in search of such a man. When he heard of a

St. Christopher, Compton Verney, England

king who was supposed to be the most powerful ruler on earth, he went to him and offered his services. One day while serving the king, he heard other men speak in awed terms of the Devil. On hearing this, Christopher went in search of the Devil; but no sooner had he found the Devil, than he learned that the Devil was afraid of someone still mightier than he.

This one the Devil feared was Christ. Christopher set out at once in search of this strong master. At last he came to a hermit who in response to his inquiry told the giant to fast. Christopher soon wearied of that. The hermit then told him if he wanted to find the Christ he should pray, but Christopher soon wearied of that and fell asleep. Finally the hermit took the giant to a river where many people drowned each year and suggested that he carry the people across to the other side. Christopher built a small hut for himself on the banks of the river. Day after day he carried people across the river safely. In his hand he carried a great pole that supported him in the water.

One night while asleep in his hut, Christopher heard a child calling. He awoke and went out in the darkness but could find no one. The same thing happened a second time. The third time the child called, Christopher at last found the child on the banks of the river. The giant placed the child on

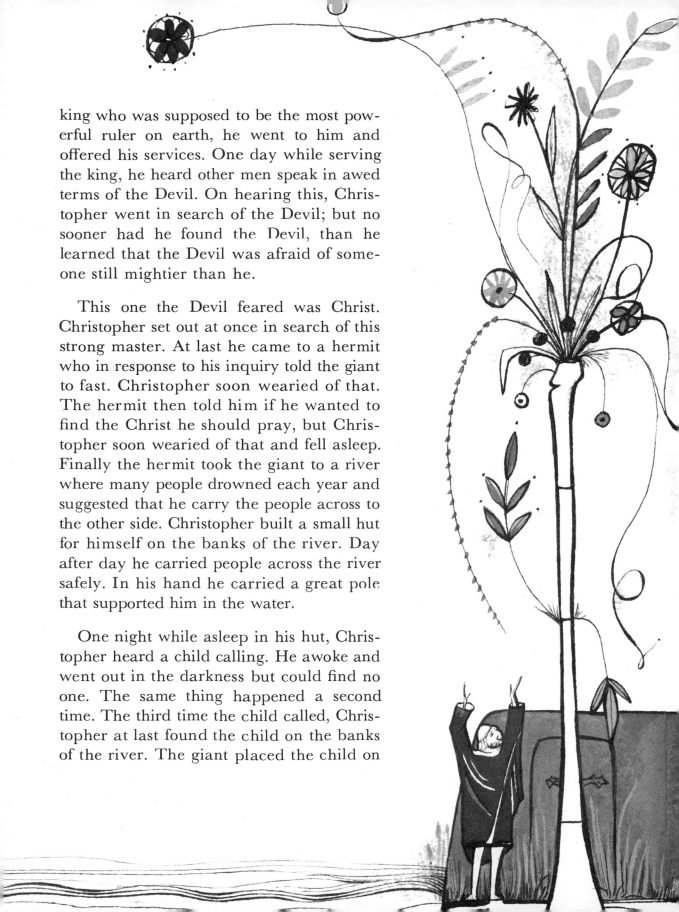

his shoulder and started across, but at each step the child became heavier, the water rose higher, and the waves became rougher. Never had Christopher had so heavy a burden or such a difficult time crossing the river. When they finally reached the other side, Christopher put the child down and said: "Never have I carried so great a burden. It would seem I was carrying the whole world." The Child answered: "Marvel not, for thou hast not only borne all the world, but borne Him that created it. I am Jesus Christ."

The child, to prove to Christopher that what he said was true, told him to plant his pole in the earth by his hut and the next day it would have flowers and fruit. The child vanished. Christopher did as the child commanded; and when he arose the following morning, he found his staff bearing flowers, leaves, and dates.

MORLEY CHURCH

The north window at the Morley church near Derby, England, tells an unusual story, that of Robert of Dale. There are seven compartments to the window. They show, in order: Sir Robert shooting a deer; the people complaining to the king; Sir Robert complaining to the king about the deer; Sir Robert catching the deer; the keepers reporting that the deer was caught; the king giving Sir Robert some ground to plow

with a deer; and Sir Robert plowing with a deer. The inscriptions under the pictures begin: "Ste Robert shooteth the Deere eatying hys corne." The legend is easily understood; and one can plainly see that the deer were ruining Sir Robert's crops. He went out to kill them, although this was against the law. Because of this, he was summoned before the king; but after he told his story, Sir Robert was pardoned. The king promised that Robert could have as much land as he could plow between two suns, that is, in one day.

GLOUCESTER CATHEDRAL

The Battle of Crecy

In the eastern end of Gloucester Cathedral there is a window that tells a story that makes the English very proud. It is the story of the Battle of Crecy in which a small English army defeated a large French army.

Edward III and his young son, the Black Prince, were invading France and had been successful in reaching the very gates of Paris when they were turned back by the French. At Crecy the Englishmen had to make a stand against a large French force.

Legend says that the French had hired 15,000 crossbowmen to drive the English from the French soil. Suddenly a storm broke; there was much lightning and thunder and rain. The bowmen were frightened;

but even worse, when the rain stopped and they were ordered to shoot at the English, their bowstrings were rainsoaked and useless. The English archers, whose bows were protected in watertight cases, drew their bows and quickly defeated the helpless army of France.

The Black Prince, although only sixteen years of age, led the charge. His father, the king, watched from a high hill because he wanted his son to have the victory. That evening around the campfire, in view of the entire army, the king embraced his son and praised him for his part in the battle.

ST. JOHN THE DIVINE

Stories are told not only in stained glass windows of Europe. Many windows in America tell stories of history, legends of saints, and tales from the Bible. Some of the loveliest windows in America are in the Cathedral of St. John the Divine in New York City.

Lafayette

Among the stories told in the historical windows at St. John the Divine is the story of Lafayette. He was a boy of nineteen when he came to America to fight against England. During the war he and George Washington became good friends.

In 1824 Lafayette, an old man, returned to the United States and was welcomed in every state and territory with receptions, dinners, and balls. It was at one of these receptions that an old soldier clad in a worn continental uniform came along the receiving line. He carried an ancient musket and across his shoulder was a piece of a blanket. Lafayette was touched by the sight. The old soldier saluted Lafayette and asked if he remembered him. Lafayette had to admit that he couldn't recall meeting the soldier. The soldier asked if he remembered the snow and cold at Valley Forge. At that Lafayette replied, "I shall never forget them." The old soldier then told how one bitter night Lafayette was going the rounds at Valley Forge when he came upon a sentry without stockings and adequate clothing. The sentry was ordered to go to Lafayette's own hut where there were stockings, a blanket, and some warm food. The soldier was to put on the stockings, eat the food, and bring the blanket to Lafayette. In the meantime Lafayette took the sentry's place as guard. When the soldier returned with the blanket, Lafayette cut it in two and gave the sentry half.

"This is the half you gave to me as the sentry that night. You saved my life," the old man finished.

St. George and the Dragon

St. George and the Dragon is a familiar legend to a great many, for it has been told often in story and song. Before it ever reached America, it was told to children in France and England in stained glass. Now in a window at St. John's the Divine in New York City, American children can see it, too.

A monstrous dragon once dwelt in a great swamp. Each year the city nearby sent sheep to the dragon so that it would not molest the people. If they failed to send the sheep, the dragon approached the walls of the city and poisoned the air with its terrible breath. No one wanted this; so when sheep were not available, a boy or a girl had to be sacrificed.

One year there were no sheep; and when the lots were cast, the daughter of the king was chosen to be sacrificed to the dragon. The people were distressed. For eight days they tried to think of a way to save the princess, but no way was found. On the ninth day the princess bade farewell to her family and her friends and set out for the lair of the dragon.

On this same day St. George was riding toward the city. He saw the beautiful girl with tears streaming down her face. Dismounting, he asked what troubled her. Her story was hardly told when the dragon was heard approaching from the swamp. The princess begged St. George to leap on his horse and flee while there was yet time. Instead St. George took his lance, approached the dragon, pierced his scaly hide, and pinned him to the ground. Then St. George told the princess to tie her sash around the dragon's neck. She did, and at once the dragon was tamed. He followed the girl like a dog back into the city.

Monsters and dragons used in legends are thought to be symbols of paganism and are always overcome by a religious man.

MAKE YOUR OWN "STAINED GLASS"

The beauty of stained glass need not be found only in large church windows, and it need not be expensive. If you would like a stained glass window in your room at home, at school, or at church you can have one by making it yourself.

The easiest kind of stained glass window to make is made with black construction paper and tracing paper or tissue paper.

Take a piece of black, nine by twelve construction paper. Draw a border of about one inch in width all around the outside of the paper. Decide on the design you want for your window and draw it on the black paper, making the lines about one fourth of an inch wide so they will not break when the design is cut out. The heavy lines must all connect with each other or with the border. After the design is all drawn, cut out all parts inside the border and the heavy lines, using very sharp scissors. Paste the cut out design on tracing paper, or on white tissue paper. Color the tracing or tissue paper with crayons or water colors. Bright colors are best. Tape your "stained glass" to the window.

Many windows in churches, schools, and homes are made up of small panes of glass. If this is the kind you have, cut pieces of black construction paper the size of the window panes. Make the "stained glass" just as above. You and all your friends can work on a window like this. Each can make "stained glass" for a different window pane. At Christmas time, for example, one person can make the angels, another the shepherds, another the wise men. Together you can fill all the windows.

Another method of making "stained glass" either for small panes or a large window uses heavy brown paper. The paper should be cut a little larger than the space it is to cover. Draw with white chalk on the paper the figures or design you desire. Color the background with crayons, using black crayon to represent the leading in the window. Then soak a piece of cotton in mineral oil and rub it all over the paper, except the black areas that represent the leading. This will make the paper translucent. Finally melt the wax in the crayons by pressing the picture with a hot iron on the wrong side of the picture. Original pictures like this can be real conversation pieces.

A group can work on different parts of a design for a large window. A really large one will need a wooden or heavy cardboard frame. Heavy tissue paper painted with poster paints can be used on the front. Make a miniature window with many small panels first so that each group working on the project will know just how their section will fit into the whole pattern. Each group, or individual, should then paint their part of the picture on a piece of tissue paper cut to the right size. When each group has completed its section, black strips of heavy paper can be used to join the small units. When all of the pieces are put together, the whole can be glued to the frame. The frame can then be fastened to the window.

A stained glass window screen is good for background scenery for some plays. Use a large piece of tissue paper, the size you want the finished screen to be. Mark off the tissue paper into squares. In each square draw a cross, symbol, or some design. Paint each square with water colors and when dry use black India ink to outline the square and the design. The India ink will make your design look like a regular stained glass window. Also it will cover up any paint that may have run over. When dry, coat both sides of the paper with clear lacquer. This makes the paper stiff and easier to handle. Use heavy cardboard to frame the window. Try placing it in front of a lamp, but not close enough to burn.

If you do not feel that you can make an original design, select a clear printed picture that does not have too much detail and use it. Fasten tissue paper over the picture and fasten it all to something solid. Using water colors, copy the picture on the tissue. If you use more than one color, be sure that the first is dry before you use the second. Keep the paint thick. Thin paint will make the tissue wrinkle. Put a little scouring powder in the paint if you want a raised surface. When the picture is finished, cut it out carefully, a little beyond the outline, and tape it to the window.

Adapted from stained glass by Bo Beskow, Skara Cathedral, England

An easier way to make a stained glass design is to take a piece of paper, wet it slightly with clear water, and put daubs of water colors here and there on it. Crumple the paper. Then open it. The colors will have run together and there will be different shades of unusual designs. Fasten the paper to a black frame, and you have a window.

Making a window of real glass is much more difficult and requires tools that are often not available. If you have the equipment needed, however, and want to try, the results can be very rewarding.

If the glass you have available is plain window glass, have someone cut it to the size you want. This can be done with glass cutters or by tapping it gently with a hammer. When the glass is cut, paint on it the design you want.

Or you may want to try using scrap colored glass. Arrange the colored bits to form a design on a piece of clear glass cut the size you want. Then glue the scraps in place on the plain glass, leaving a space around each piece. After the glue is dry, pour a thin solution of plaster of Paris into the space around each small piece of glass. After the plaster dries wipe away any excess. Bind the edges with black masking tape or black adhesive tape, or place in a wooden frame.

Your "stained glass" windows, however you make them, may not rival those of Chartres or some of our more modern churches in beauty, but they will add color and brightness to the place where they are displayed. Best of all you will have the delight of making them and may feel some of the joy that craftsmen of old must have felt when they completed their windows.

BIBLIOGRAPHY

Adams, Henry, *Mont-Saint-Michel and Chartres*, Houghton Mifflin Co., N.Y., 1936.

Anderson, Robert Gordon, *Biography of a Cathedral*, Longmans, Green & Co., N.Y., 1945.

Arnold, Hugh, *Stained Glass of the Middle Ages*, A. & C. Black, London, 1937.

Aubert, Marcel, *French Cathedral Windows*, Oxford University Press, London, 1939.

Caxton, William, *The Golden Legend*, Dent & Co., London, 1900.

Clark, Sidney, *Today in Cathedral France*, Robert McBride & Co., N.Y., 1948.

Clement, Silvain, *Vitraux de Bourges*, Tardy-Pigelet, Bourges, 1900.

Coe, Fanny, *Third Book of Stories for the Story Teller*, Houghton Mifflin, N.Y., 1920.

Day, Lewis, *Windows*, B. T. Batsford, London, 1902.

Delaporte, Y., *Les Vitraux de la Cathedrale de Chartres*, E. Houvet, Chartres, 1926.

Diamond, Freda, *Story of Glass*, Harcourt Brace & Co., N.Y., 1953.

Dunney, Joseph, *Church History in the Light of the Saints*, Macmillan, N.Y., 1944.

Eden, Sydney, *Ancient Stained and Painted Glass*, University Press, Cambridge, 1933.

Editors of Life, *Life's Picture History of Western Man*, Simon & Schuster, N.Y., 1951.

Farjeon, Eleanor, *Ten Saints*, Walck, N.Y., 1936.

Gardner, Helen, *Art Through the Ages*, Harcourt, Brace & Co., N.Y., 1948.

Grodecki, Louis, *Stained Glass of French Churches*, L. Drummond, London, 1948.

Joyce, J. G., *The Fairford Windows*, Arundel Society, London, 1872.

Luce, Clare Booth, *Saints for Now*, Sheed & Ward, N.Y., 1952.

Pennell, Mrs. Elizabeth (Robins), *French Cathedrals*, Century Co., N.Y., 1909.

Prentice, Sartell, *The Voices of the Cathedral*, W. Morrow & Co., N.Y., 1938.

Rackham, Bernard, *Ancient Glass of Canterbury Cathedral*, Lund Humphries, London, 1949.

Sherrill, Charles Hitchcock, *Stained Glass Tours in England*, J. Lane Co., London, 1940.

Sherrill, Charles Hitchcock, *Stained Glass Tours in France*, J. Lane Co., London, 1908.

Sowers, Robert, *The Lost Art*, Wittenborn, N.Y., 1954.

Temko, Allan, *Notre Dame of Paris*, Viking, N.Y., 1955.

Thurston, Herbert & Attwater, Donald, *Butler's Lives of the Saints*, vol. I, II, III, IV, P. J. Kennedy & Sons, N.Y., 1956.